THE COLDEST PLACE ON EARTH

Stage 1

At the South Pole today there is a building called the Amundsen-Scott Station. Inside the building it is warm and people live and work there both in summer and in winter. Planes fly easily to and from the station, and the rest of the world is only a few hours away. But walk five hundred metres away from the station, and Antarctica is once again the coldest, emptiest place on earth.

In 1911 there were no planes and no buildings at the South Pole. There was nothing. Only snow and ice and wind. There was no British flag, and no Norwegian flag. But across the ice, men were moving slowly south. Scott's men had ponies, and Amundsen's men had dogs and skis. The temperatures were –30° Centigrade and worse. The men were tired, hungry, cold . . . Who was going to be the first man at the South Pole?

Inside the Amundsen-Scott station today, there are some words written on the wall – words that Captain Scott wrote in his diary in 1912:

'Great God! This is an awful place.'

Tim Vicary, the author of this story, is an experienced teacher and writer. He lives and works in York, in the north of England.

OXFORD BOOKWORMS

OXFORD BOOKWORMS

For a full list of titles in all the Oxford Bookworms series, please refer to the *Oxford English* catalogue.

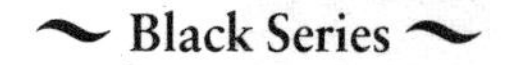

Black Series

Titles available include:

Stage 1 (400 headwords)
*The Elephant Man *Tim Vicary*
*The Monkey's Paw *W. W. Jacobs*
Under the Moon *Rowena Akinyemi*
*The Phantom of the Opera *Jennifer Bassett*

Stage 2 (700 headwords)
*Sherlock Holmes Short Stories *Sir Arthur Conan Doyle*
*Voodoo Island *Michael Duckworth*
*New Yorkers *O. Henry* (short stories)

Stage 3 (1000 headwords)
*Skyjack! *Tim Vicary*
Love Story *Erich Segal*
Tooth and Claw *Saki* (short stories)
Wyatt's Hurricane *Desmond Bagley*

Stage 4 (1400 headwords)
*The Hound of the Baskervilles *Sir Arthur Conan Doyle*
*Three Men in a Boat *Jerome K. Jerome*
The Big Sleep *Raymond Chandler*

Stage 5 (1800 headwords)
*Ghost Stories *retold by Rosemary Border*
The Dead of Jericho *Colin Dexter*
*Wuthering Heights *Emily Brontë*
I, Robot *Isaac Asimov* (short stories)

Stage 6 (2500 headwords)
*Tess of the d'Urbervilles *Thomas Hardy*
Cry Freedom *John Briley*
Meteor *John Wyndham* (short stories)
Deadheads *Reginald Hill*

Many other titles available, both classic and modern.
**Cassettes available for these titles.*

Green Series

Adaptations of classic and modern stories for younger readers.
Titles available include:

Stage 2 (700 headwords)
*Robinson Crusoe *Daniel Defoe*
*Alice's Adventures in Wonderland *Lewis Carroll*
Too Old to Rock and Roll *Jan Mark* (short stories)

Stage 3 (1000 headwords)
*The Prisoner of Zenda *Anthony Hope*
*The Secret Garden *Frances Hodgson Burnett*
On the Edge *Gillian Cross*

Stage 4 (1400 headwords)
*Treasure Island *Robert Louis Stevenson*
*Gulliver's Travels *Jonathan Swift*
A Tale of Two Cities *Charles Dickens*
The Silver Sword *Ian Serraillier*

OXFORD BOOKWORMS COLLECTION

Fiction by well-known authors, both classic and modern.
Texts are not abridged or simplified in any way. Titles available include:

From the Cradle to the Grave
(short stories by *Saki, Evelyn Waugh, Roald Dahl, Susan Hill, Somerset Maugham, H. E. Bates, Frank Sargeson, Raymond Carver*)

Crime Never Pays
(short stories by *Agatha Christie, Graham Greene, Ruth Rendell, Angela Noel, Dorothy L. Sayers, Margery Allingham, Sir Arthur Conan Doyle, Patricia Highsmith*)

Tim Vicary

OXFORD UNIVERSITY PRESS

Oxford University Press
Great Clarendon Street, Oxford OX2 6DP

Oxford New York
Athens Auckland Bangkok Bogota Bombay
Buenos Aires Calcutta Cape Town Dar es Salaam Delhi
Florence Hong Kong Istanbul Karachi Kuala Lumpur
Madras Madrid Melbourne Mexico City Nairobi
Paris Singapore Taipei Tokyo Toronto

and associated companies in
Berlin Ibadan

OXFORD and OXFORD ENGLISH
are trade marks of Oxford University Press

ISBN 0 19 422690 5

First published 1992
Sixth impression 1997

We would like to thank the following for their permission to reproduce photographs:

Norsk Polarinstitutt pages 15, 17, 25, 32
Popperfoto pages 3, 7, 10, 14, 18, 23, 29, 30, 31, 35, 36, 38
The Royal Geographical Society pages 2, 11, 12, 19, 20, 34

Typeset by Oxuniprint
Printed in Great Britain
by Clays Ltd, St Ives plc

Chapter 1

Two Ships

The race began in the summer of 1910.

On June 1st, in London, a black ship, the *Terra Nova*, went down the river Thames to the sea. Thousands of people stood by the river to watch it. They were all excited and happy.

On the *Terra Nova*, Captain Robert Falcon Scott smiled quietly. It was a very important day for him. He was a strong man, not very tall, in the blue clothes of a captain. He was forty-one years old, but he had a young face, like a boy. His eyes were dark and quiet.

One man on the ship, Titus Oates, smiled at Scott.

'What an exciting day, Captain!' he said. 'Look at those people! I feel like an important man!'

Scott laughed. 'You *are* important, Titus,' he said. 'And you're going to be famous, too. We all are. Do you see this flag?' He looked at the big British flag at the back of the ship, and smiled at Oates. 'That flag is coming with us,' he said. 'In the Antarctic, I'm going to carry it under my clothes. We're going to be the first men at the South Pole, and that flag is going to be first, too!'

* * * * *

Five days later, on June 6th, a man opened the door of his wooden house in Norway. He was a tall man, with a long face.

Captain Robert Falcon Scott

He waited outside the house for a minute. Everything was very quiet. He could see no houses, only mountains, trees, and water. It was nearly dark. The sky was black over the mountains.

The man smiled, and walked quickly away from the house, down to the sea. In the water, a big wooden ship waited for him. The man got onto the ship, and talked and laughed quietly with his friends.

The ship's name was *Fram*, and the man was Roald Amundsen. The *Fram* was the most beautiful ship on earth,

Roald Amundsen

Amundsen thought. His friends were the best skiers on earth, too. One of them, Olav Bjaaland, smiled at him.

'North Pole, here we come, Captain,' he said.

'Yes.' Amundsen said. His friends could not see his face in the dark. '*Fram* is going to the Arctic.'

Everyone on the *Fram* was ready to go to the North Pole, to the Arctic. Amundsen wanted to go there, too. But first he wanted to go south. His friends didn't know that.

At midnight on June 6th, the *Fram* moved quietly away from Amundsen's house, out to sea.

Chapter 2

The Race

The *Fram* went to an island in the south of Norway. It was a very little island, with only one small wooden house, two trees – and nearly a hundred dogs.

'Look at that!' Bjaaland said. 'It's an island of dogs! There are dogs in the water, near the trees, on the house – dogs everywhere!'

Two men came out of the house. 'Hassel! Lindstrøm!' Amundsen said. 'It's good to see you! How many dogs do you have for me?'

'Ninety-nine, Roald,' said Hassel. 'The best ninety-nine dogs from Greenland. And they're very happy! They don't work;

they just eat and play all day! They're having a wonderful summer here!'

'Good, good.' Amundsen laughed. 'But that's finished now. Hey, Bjaaland! Stop laughing – come down here and help me. Let's get all these dogs onto the ship!'

It was not easy. The dogs were fat and strong, and they didn't want to go on the ship. But at last, after three hours' hard work, all ninety-nine were on the ship, and the *Fram* went out to sea again.

The men were not happy. The weather was bad, the dogs were dirty, and some of the men were ill. They began to ask questions.

'Why are we bringing dogs with us?' asked one man, Johansen. 'We're going thousands of kilometres south, past Cape Horn, and then north to Alaska. Why not wait, and get dogs in Alaska?'

'Don't ask me,' said his friend, Helmer Hanssen, 'I don't understand it.'

The men talked for a long time. Then, on September 9th, Amundsen called everyone to the back of the ship. He stood quietly and looked at them. Behind him was a big map. It was not a map of the Arctic. It was a map of Antarctica.

Bjaaland looked at Helmer Hanssen, and laughed. Then Amundsen began to speak.

'Boys,' he said. 'I know you are unhappy. You often ask me difficult questions, and I don't answer. Well, I'm going to answer all those questions now, today.

'We began to work for this journey two years ago. Then, we wanted to be the first men at the North Pole. But last year, Peary, an American, found the North Pole. So America was first to the North Pole, not Norway. We're going there, but we're too late.'

'I don't understand this,' Bjaaland thought. 'Why is Amundsen talking about the North Pole, with a map of Antarctica behind him?'

Amundsen stopped for a minute, and looked at all the men slowly. No one said anything.

'We have to go a long way south before we get to Alaska,' he said. 'Very near Antarctica, you know. And Captain Scott, the Englishman, is going to the South Pole this year. He wants to put his British flag there. An American flag at the North Pole, a British flag at the South Pole.'

Bjaaland began to understand. He started to smile and couldn't stop. He was warm and excited.

'Well, boys,' Amundsen said slowly. 'Do we want the British to put their flag at the South Pole first? How fast can we travel? We have a lot of dogs, and some of the most wonderful skiers on earth – Bjaaland here is the best in Norway! So I have an idea, boys. Let's go to the South Pole, and put the Norwegian flag there before the British! What do you say?'

For a minute or two it was very quiet. Amundsen waited, and the men watched him and thought. Then Bjaaland laughed.

'Yes!' he said. 'Why not? It's a ski race, isn't it, and the English can't ski! It's a wonderful idea, of course! Let's go!'

Chapter 3

The Ponies

On October 27th, the *Terra Nova* arrived in Wellington, New Zealand. When Scott came off the ship, a newspaper man walked up to him.

'Captain Scott! Captain Scott! Can I talk to you, please!' he said.

Terra Nova

Scott stopped and smiled. 'Yes, of course,' he said. 'What do you want to know?'

'Are you going to win?' the man asked.

'Win?' Scott asked. 'Win what?'

'Win the race to the South Pole, of course,' the newspaper man said. 'It's a race between you and Amundsen, now. Look at this!' He gave a newspaper to Scott. Scott looked at it. It said:

FRAM RACES SCOTT TO SOUTH POLE

'We're going to win!' says Amundsen

Scott's face went white. 'Give me that!' he said. He took the newspaper and read it carefully. The newspaper man watched him, and waited. 'Well, Captain Scott,' he said at last. 'Who's going to win this race? Tell me that!'

Scott looked at him angrily. 'This is stupid!' he said. 'It's not a race! I came here to learn about the Antarctic – I'm not interested in Amundsen, or in races!' Then he walked back onto his ship, with the newspaper in his hand.

Later that day, he talked to his men. He gave them the newspaper, and laughed.

'It doesn't matter,' he said. 'We're in front of Amundsen, and we have more men, and more money. He has only eight men, and a lot of dogs. I know about dogs – they don't work in the Antarctic. We have sixteen men and the new motor sledges – they are much better. And tomorrow the ponies are coming. We need ponies, motor sledges, and good strong British men – that's all. Forget about Amundsen! He's not important!'

Scott asked Oates to look after the ponies, but he did not let Oates buy them. When Oates first saw the ponies, in New Zealand, he was very unhappy. Most of the ponies were old, and some of them were ill.

'They're beautiful ponies, Titus,' Scott said. 'They come from China – they're wonderful ponies!'

Oates looked at them angrily, and said nothing. Then he asked: 'Where is their food, Captain?'

'Here!' Scott opened a door.

Oates looked inside. He thought for a minute. 'We need more food than this, Captain Scott! These ponies are going to work in the coldest place on earth – they need a lot of food – more than this!'

Scott smiled quietly. 'We can't take more food on this ship, Titus. Where can we put it? But it doesn't matter, old boy. They're very strong ponies, you know. The best ponies on earth.'

Later that night, Oates wrote a letter to his mother. *There are nineteen ponies on the* Terra Nova *now*, he wrote. *All the ponies are in a small room at the front of the ship. We eat our food in the room under the ponies, so our table is often wet and dirty. Scott makes a lot of mistakes, I think, and Antarctica is a very dangerous place.*

Oates and the ponies on the Terra Nova

Chapter 4

Food Depots

The two ships, *Terra Nova* and *Fram*, arrived in Antarctica, in January 1911, at the end of summer. The Englishmen and the Norwegians wanted to stay on the ice all winter. They wanted to be ready to go to the South Pole at the beginning of the next Antarctic summer.

The dogs pulled the Norwegians' sledges. They ran quickly over the snow and pulled the big sledges from the ship onto the ice. The men ran beside them on skis.

They put a big wooden house on the ice. The house was full of food, and skis, and sledges. They called it Framheim.

Framheim

Outside the house, the dogs lived in holes under the snow. When the house was ready, the men made their first journey south.

Before the winter, they wanted to take a lot of food south, and leave it in depots. For the long journey to the Pole, they needed a lot of food, and they couldn't carry it all with them. On February 10th, five men, three sledges, eighteen dogs, and half a tonne of food left Framheim and went south.

It was easy. The weather was warm for the Antarctic, between –7° Centigrade and –17° Centigrade. The snow was good, and the dogs and skis went fast. They went fifty or sixty kilometres every day. After four days they reached 80° South, and made the first depot.

Amundsen made his depot very carefully. It was very important to find it again, next summer. So he put a big black

The first depot

flag on top. Then he put ten flags to the east of the depot – each flag half a kilometre from the next – and ten flags to the west. So there were flags for five kilometres to the left of the depot, and five kilometres to the right.

Then they went back to Framheim, and took some more food south, this time to 82° South.

This time it was harder. The temperature was sometimes –40° Centigrade, and there were strong winds with a lot of snow. The dogs and men were very tired, and the tents and boots were bad. At the second depot, they put out sixty flags, to help them find it again.

They came back to Framheim on March 23rd. It was nearly winter in the Antarctic. Their ship *Fram* was far away now, near South America. They were alone on the ice.

* * * * *

Oates went with Scott to make the first British depot. They left Cape Evans on January 25th. There were thirteen men, eight ponies, and twenty-six dogs. The dogs were faster than the ponies – they ran quickly over the top of the snow, but the ponies' feet went through it. Every morning the ponies started first, and the dogs started two hours later, because they ran faster. At night, the dogs made warm holes under the snow, but the ponies stood on top of the snow. It was –20° Centigrade.

After fifteen days Oates talked to Scott. There was a strong wind, and the two men's faces were white with snow.

'Three of these ponies are ill, Captain,' Oates said. 'They can't go on.'

'Don't be stupid, Oates,' Scott answered. 'They're good strong animals – the best ponies on earth.'

'Not these three,' Oates said. 'They're ill, and unhappy, and now they can't walk. Let's kill them, and leave the meat here, in the snow. We can eat it, or the dogs can.'

'Of course not!' Scott said angrily. 'These ponies are our friends, they work hard for us. I don't kill my friends!'

Three days later, two of the ponies were dead.

Scott's men were slower than Amundsen's; it took them twenty-four days to get to 80° South. They made a big depot there, and put one large black flag on top of it. Then they went back to Cape Evans.

Terra Nova *at Cape Evans*

Their camp was on an island in the ice, and the sea ice moved sometimes. There were holes in the ice, and black sea water under it. One day seven ponies went through the ice into the sea, and died. One motor sledge also went into the sea.

Chapter 5

A Long Cold Winter

It was dark for four months. Outside the wooden house at Framheim, it was often –60° Centigrade. The dogs lived in warm holes under the snow. The men stayed in the house, and worked in their rooms under the snow.

Bjaaland changed a lot of things on the sledges.

The skis and sledges came from the best shops in Norway, but Bjaaland wasn't happy with them. He changed a lot of things on the skis and sledges. Soon the sledges were stronger than before. The skis were better and faster, too.

All the Norwegians

worked hard. They looked after their dogs, and worked on their equipment – the sledges, skis, tents. Every day they thought about their journey to the Pole, and talked about it. And every day, Amundsen thought about Scott. One day, in midwinter, he talked to his men.

'Let's start early, before Scott,' Amundsen said. 'Remember, Scott has more men than us, and he has motor sledges, too. Perhaps they can go faster than us.'

Bjaaland laughed. 'Oh no, they can't go faster than me,' he said. 'On snow, nothing can go faster than a good man on skis.'

'We don't know,' Amundsen said. 'You're the best skier in Norway, but you get tired, and dogs get tired, too. Motor sledges don't get tired. They can go all day and all night.'

Johansen laughed angrily. 'That's stupid,' he said. 'Perhaps the motor sledges can go all night, but the Englishmen can't. The English can't win, Roald – they don't understand snow, but we do. And they're too slow.'

'Perhaps,' Amundsen said. 'But I want to win this race. So we're going to start early! Do you understand?'

It was quiet and warm inside Framheim. Bjaaland looked at Amundsen, and though about the long, cold journey in front of him. He thought about the dogs in their holes under the snow, and listened to the wind over the house. 'When, Roald?' he said quietly.

'On August 24th. The sun comes back on that day. We start then.'

'But we can't!' Johansen said. He looked angry, and

Inside Framheim

unhappy. 'That's too early! We can't start then – it's dangerous and stupid!'

Amundsen looked at Johansen coldly. 'You're wrong, Johansen,' he said. 'We want to win, remember? So we start on August 24th.'

Bjaaland listened to the winter wind outside.

* * * * *

In Scott's camp, at Cape Evans, no one talked about Amundsen and no one worked hard. They had good food, and they played football on the snow. They wrote a newspaper – *The South Polar*

In Scott's camp at Cape Evans they had good food.

Times – and read books. No one learnt to ski, no one worked on the motor sledges. Twice, men went for long journeys across the snow. They walked, and pulled the sledges themselves. Oates stayed at Cape Evans and looked after his ponies.

Over the window in Cape Evans, Scott put a map of Antarctica. With a pen, he made a line from Cape Evans to the South Pole, and he put a little British Flag at the Pole. Under the map, Scott wrote the day for the start of their journey.

We start on November 3rd, he wrote.

We start on November 3rd, *he wrote*.

Chapter 6

A Bad Start

On August 23rd, the Norwegians' sledges were ready. They took them outside, and the dogs pulled them across the ice. The sun came up for a half an hour, but it was too cold: –46° Centigrade. They could not travel in that weather. They went back to Framheim and waited.

They waited two weeks, until September 8th. Then, with the temperature at –37° Centigrade, they started. They ran happily across the snow to the south – eight men, seven sledges, and eighty-six dogs. Only Lindstrøm, the cook, stayed behind in Framheim.

At first everything went well.

At first everything went well. They went twenty-eight kilometres on Saturday, and twenty-eight kilometres on Sunday. It was easy.

Then, on Monday, the temperature went down – to –56° Centigrade. There was white fog in front of their faces. They couldn't see anything. But they travelled twenty-eight kilometres.

That night, in their tents, they nearly died of cold. Next day, they stopped and made snow houses. Inside the snow houses, it was warm. But everyone was unhappy.

'I told you, Roald!' Johansen said. 'Even September is too early! We can't travel in this cold. Do you want us to die? Let's go back and wait for better weather.'

Amundsen was very angry. He was angry with Johansen, but he was angry with himself, too. He knew Johansen was right.

'All right,' he said slowly. 'We can go on to the depot at 80° South, leave the food there, and then go back. We can't do more than that.'

It was thirty-seven kilometres to the depot. The wind was in their faces all day. Two dogs died on the way. At the depot, they did not stop. They put out the food and the flags, turned round, and went north.

At last the wind was behind them. The dogs ran quickly, and the men sat on the empty sledges. They went faster and faster. It was like a race. Amundsen was on Wisting's sledge, and soon he, Wisting, and Hanssen were three or four kilometres in front. Soon they were alone. They travelled seventy-five kilometres in nine hours, and they reached Framheim at four o'clock that afternoon.

Bjaaland arrived two hours later, with two more men. But the last two – Johansen and Prestrud – went more slowly. Their dogs were tired, their feet were wet and cold, they had no food, and they were alone in the dark. The temperature was –51° Centigrade. They reached Framheim at midnight.

Next morning, Johansen was angry. In front of everyone, he said: 'You were wrong, Roald. September was too early. I told you but you didn't listen. And then you left us alone and we nearly died in the cold! You're a bad captain – I'm a better captain than you are!'

Amundsen was very angry. But at first he said nothing, because he knew that Johansen was right. Then, that evening, he gave a letter to Johansen. It said:

You aren't coming to the Pole with me. When I go south, you can take some dogs and go east to King Edward VII Land. You can go with Prestrud and Stubberud. You can be the first men to go there – but not to the South Pole!

The Norwegians stayed in Framheim and waited. They lay in bed, listened to the wind outside, and thought about Scott and his motor sledges.

Chapter 7

Motor Sledges and Mountains

Scott had two motor sledges now. They were the first motor sledges in the Antarctic – the first on earth. On October 24th, the motor sledges started south from Cape Evans. Four men went with them, but Scott stayed at Cape Evans for another week.

Oates was unhappy. He wrote to his mother: *We had a very bad winter here. I don't like Scott. We were here all winter, but he didn't learn to ski, or to drive dogs. Our equipment is bad, and he doesn't think about other people. I'm going to sleep in his tent on the journey, but I don't want to.*

The first motor sledge in Antarctica

On November 1st Scott and Oates and six more men left Cape Evans with eight sledges and eight ponies. The ponies walked slowly because their feet went down into the snow. It was hard work for them and they got tired very quickly. They travelled thirteen or fourteen kilometres in a day.

Behind the ponies came Meares with one sledge and some dogs. Meares knew how to drive dogs. Every day, Meares started two hours after the ponies, and arrived two hours before them.

After five days, they found the motor sledges.

* * * * *

The Norwegians began again on October 20th. There were five men this time – Amundsen, Bjaaland, Wisting, Hassel, and Hanssen. They had four sledges, and forty-eight dogs.

There was a lot of wind and fog. On the first day, Wisting's sledge suddenly stopped, and the back went down. 'Come on, you dogs!' he said angrily. 'Pull! Pull!' At first nothing happened; then, slowly, the sledge moved again. Wisting looked down, over the side of the sledge. Under the snow, there was a fifty metre hole.

'Did you see that?' Amundsen said. 'The ice wants to eat us – men, dogs, sledges, everything.'

On the fourth day they reached the depot at 80° South. There was a bad snowstorm, but they found the flags easily. Next day the men stayed in their tents, and the dogs played in their holes under the snow. They were all happy. They had a lot of food, they had good equipment, and they were warm. They could travel fast.

The depot at 80° South.

Next morning, the snowstorm stopped, and the journey began again. *Today, everything is wonderful*, Bjaaland wrote in his diary. *But where is Scott? In front of us, or behind?*

* * * * *

There was no one with the motor sledges; they were broken. Scott looked at them angrily.

'It doesn't matter,' he said. 'Teddy Evans and his men are in front of us. They're good men – they're pulling their sledges themselves. We can get to the Pole on foot.'

Oates looked at Meares. Oates and the ponies were tired, but Meares and his dogs were not. The snow was home for them.

That night, Oates wrote: *Three motor sledges at £1,000 each, 19 ponies at £5 each, 32 dogs at £1.50 each. Well, it's not my money, it's Scott's.*

On November 21st, one of the ponies died.

* * * * *

On November 11th, the Norwegians saw the mountains.

The mountains were very high – some of the highest on earth. Bjaaland smiled.

'There is good skiing up there, Roald,' he said. 'But can dogs get up there too?'

'Of course they can,' Amundsen said. 'Come on.'

They left Hanssen with the dogs, and skied a little way up the mountains. It was difficult, but the mountains were big and beautiful. Behind the mountains, Amundsen thought there was a high plateau of ice. 'That's it,' Amundsen said. 'That's the road to the Pole. Tomorrow, we can bring the dogs and sledges up here. But now, let's have a ski race. Who can get back to camp first?'

They laughed, and skied happily down the white snow. 'This is like home,' Bjaaland thought. 'But it's bigger than Norway, and better.'

In the next four days, the dogs pulled the sledges eighty-one kilometres, and went up 3,000 metres. At last, Amundsen and Bjaaland stood on the plateau behind the mountains. They were tired, happy men.

Bjaaland looked back at the mountains. 'Can a motor sledge get up here?' he asked.

Amundsen smiled. 'No,' he said. 'I don't think so. And Scott doesn't like dogs. So his men are going to pull their sledges up these mountains themselves. Would you like to do that, Olav?'

Bjaaland didn't answer. He smiled, and skied happily away across the snow.

Chapter 8
Across the Plateau

On November 21st, the Norwegians killed thirty dogs. 'They were happy,' Amundsen said. 'And now they're going to die quickly. We need three sledges, and eighteen dogs, to go to the Pole.'

When the dogs were dead, the other dogs ate them. The men ate them, too. *They were good friends*, Bjaaland wrote in his diary. *And now they are good food.* Two days later, the dogs were fat. Then, in a snowstorm, they began the journey again.

After the snowstorm, there was fog, and in the fog, they got lost on an ice river with hundreds of big holes in it. They could see nothing, and it was very dangerous. In four days they moved nine kilometres. *But the ice is beautiful*, Bjaaland wrote. *Blue and green and white. This is a wonderful place – but I don't want to stay a long time.*

After the ice, there were strong winds and bad snowstorms. They could see nothing in front of them. But every day, they travelled twenty-five or thirty kilometres. Then, on December 9th, the sun came out. They were at 88° 23' South – 175 kilometres from the Pole.

Five more long days, Bjaaland wrote. *That's all now. But where is Scott?*

* * * * *

For four days, Scott's men stayed in their tents near the mountains. *There is a bad snowstorm outside*, Oates wrote. *It's too cold for the ponies, and our clothes and skis are bad, too.*

On December 9th, Oates killed the ponies. They were tired and ill and they could not walk up to the plateau. Then Meares and his dogs went back to Cape Evans. 'We can pull the sledges ourselves,' Scott said. 'We can do it – we're all strong men.'

There were two sledges and eight men. They went twenty-four kilometres a day. On December 31st, Scott said to Teddy Evans, and the men on the second sledge: 'You can't ski well.

'We can pull the sledges ourselves,' Scott said.

Leave your skis here.' So they pulled their sledge twenty-four kilometres without skis.

Next day, Scott went to Teddy Evans's tent. 'You are ill, Teddy,' he said. 'You can't come to the Pole. Take two men and go back, tomorrow.'

Teddy Evans was very unhappy. 'Two men, Captain?' he said. 'Why not three?'

'Because Bowers is going to come with me,' Scott said. 'He's strong – we need him.'

'But . . . you have food on your sledge for four men, not five!' Evans said. 'And Bowers has no skis!'

'I'm the Captain, Teddy!' Scott said. 'You do what I say. Take two men and leave Bowers with me!'

Oates wrote to his mother: *I am going to the Pole with Scott. I am pleased and I feel strong*. But in his diary he wrote: *My feet are very bad. They are always wet now, and they don't look good.*

On January 4th Scott's men left Teddy Evans and went on. Scott, Oates, Wilson and Edgar Evans had skis, but Bowers did not. They were 270 kilometres from the Pole.

They were 270 kilometres from the Pole.

* * * * *

December 14th 1911 was a warm, sunny day. Five Norwegians skied over the beautiful white snow. It was very quiet. No one spoke. They were excited, and happy.

'Six more kilometres,' Bjaaland thought. *Is there a British flag? I can't see a flag, but . . .*

'Look!' Hassel said. 'What's that over there?'

Bjaaland left his sledge and skied quickly away over the snow. 'What is it?' he thought. 'Is it . . .? No!'

'It's nothing!' he called. 'There's nothing there . . . nothing!'

Three kilometres, two. 'Roald!' Hanssen called to Amundsen. 'Go in front of me, please. It helps my dogs.'

'That's not true,' Bjaaland thought. 'His dogs are running well today. But Hanssen wants Amundsen to be first. The first man at the South Pole!'

They skied on and on, over the beautiful snow.

'Stop!' Amundsen said. He waited quietly for his men. 'This is it,' he said.

Bjaaland looked at him. 'But there's nothing here,' he said.

Amundsen smiled. 'Oh

'This is it,' said Amundsen.

yes there is,' he said. 'There's something very important here, Olav. Very, very important.'

'What's that, Roald?'

'Us. We're here now. Isn't that important, Olav?'

The four men stood on the snow, and looked at him. Then, slowly, they all began to laugh.

Chapter 9

The End of the Race

The Norwegians stayed two days at the Pole. They left a tent there, with a Norwegian flag on it. Inside the tent, they left some food, a letter for the King of Norway, and a letter for Scott.

The Norwegians left a tent with a flag on it.

They left some more black flags near the Pole, and one twenty-eight kilometres north. Then they skied away, back to the north.

It's a beautiful day, Bjaaland wrote. *The sun is warm, the snow is good. But the dogs run too quickly – I can't get in front of them!*

They found their depots easily. There were ten between the Pole and Framheim. Each depot had a lot of food. They laughed and skied quickly down the mountains. Often, they skied fifty kilometres a day. On Friday, January 26th, 1912, they came back to Framheim. It was four o'clock in the morning.

Inside the wooden house, Lindstrøm, the cook, was asleep. Amundsen walked quietly to his bed. 'Good morning, Lindstrøm,' he said. 'Is our coffee ready?'

* * * * *

The black flags waited at the Pole.

'What's that, Captain?' Bowers said. 'Over there?'

'Where?' Scott asked. 'What – oh my God!'

They all saw the small black flag in the snow, two kilometres in front of them. Slowly, they pulled their sledge to it.

Next day, January 17th 1912, they found the tent and the Norwegian flag. Near it, Scott took the British flag from under his clothes, and put it up. In his diary, Scott wrote: *This is a very bad day. We are all tired, and have cold feet and hands. It is –30°*

On January 17th 1912, they found the tent and the Norwegian flag.

Centigrade and there is a snowstorm. Great God! This is an awful place!

They turned north. Five tired, unhappy men, in the coldest, emptiest place on earth.

Five tired, unhappy men, in the coldest, emptiest place on earth.

* * * * *

On March 13th, 1912, Scott's wife Kathleen, looked at her morning newspaper. NORWAY'S FLAG AT SOUTH POLE, it said. She looked at it for a long time, and then began to cry.

'What's the matter?' her friend asked.

'My poor, poor husband,' Mrs Scott said. 'What's happened to him? Where is he now?'

* * * * *

Scott's men were always hungry. There were not many depots and they were difficult to find. *We need to find the next depot today*, Oates wrote. *But how can we find one black flag in all this snow? It's very difficult. And there is food for four men, not five.*

Scott's men were always hungry.

They were all tired and ill, too. Oates's feet were black now, and he could not feel them. On February 16th, Edgar Evans died.

On the 17th they were past the mountains. At the depot there they ate one of the dead ponies. Then they went on – ten, eleven, twelve kilometres a day. They were ill because their clothes were not warm and they didn't have much food. The temperature was sometimes –40° Centigrade.

On March 7th Scott looked at Oates's feet. They were big and black. 'I can't pull the sledge now,' Oates said. 'It's very difficult to walk. Am I going to lose these feet, Captain?'

Scott looked at Oates's feet, and said nothing.

On March 9th they found another depot, but there was not much food. Slowly, they walked on. Oates's feet were worse every day.

March 17th was Oates's birthday. He was thirty-two. He lay in the tent and listened to the wind outside. He was very cold, very hungry, and very very tired.

He wrote a letter to his mother and gave it to Wilson. Then he got up, and opened the door of the tent. He stopped in the door for a minute. Scott, Wilson, and Bowers looked at him. They didn't speak.

'I'm going outside for a minute,' Oates said. 'I may be some time.'

They didn't see him again.

* * * * *

At Cape Evans, the Englishmen waited. On December 11th, Meares and the dogs came back. On January 3rd, Teddy Evans and his two men arrived at Cape Evans. The *Terra Nova* came, and went. Winter began. Scott did not come.

The Englishmen waited all winter at Cape Evans. Then, on October 26th 1912, they started for the south. Two weeks later, they found a tent.

There were three bodies in the tent – Scott,

They put the bodies under the snow.

Wilson, and Bowers. They put the bodies under the snow. Then they took the men's letters and diaries, and went north to Cape Evans again.

In Scott's diary they read: *Oates died like a good Englishman. We all did. Please, remember us, and look after our families. We did our best.*

No one found Oates's body. But he is there, somewhere, under the snow and the wind, in the coldest, emptiest place on earth.

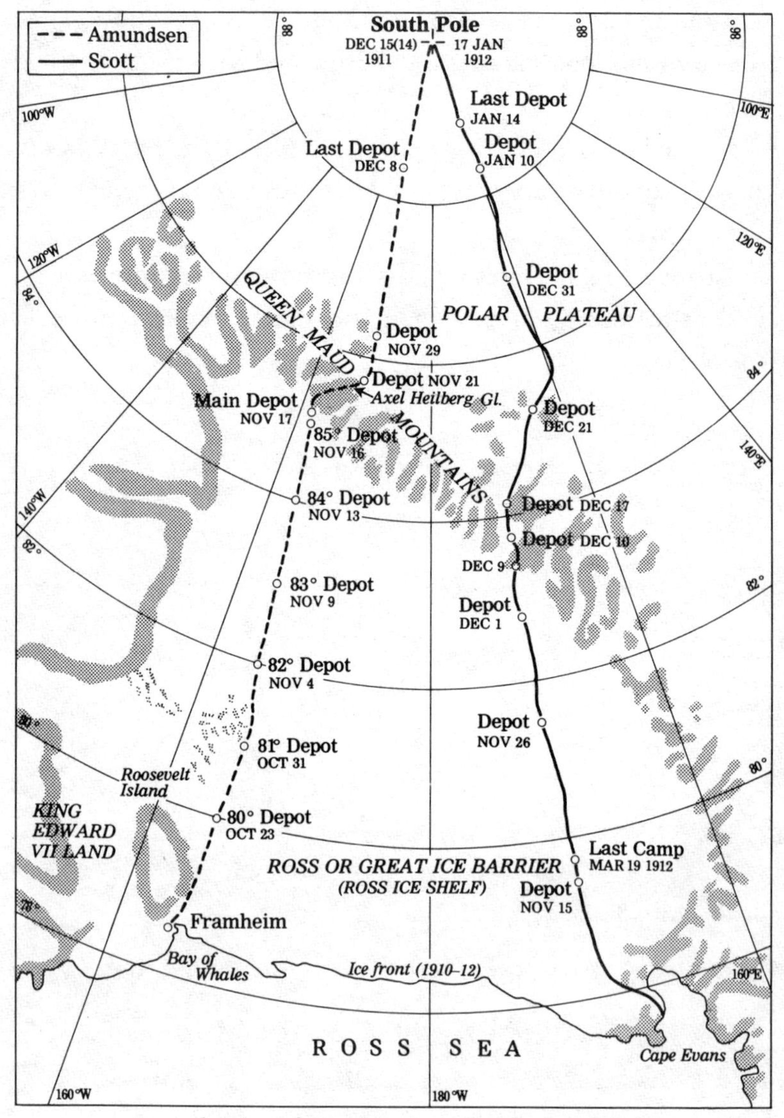

Amundsen's and Scott's journeys to the South Pole.

Exercises

A Checking your understanding

Chapters 1, 2 and 3 *Who said this?*

1 'I feel like an important man.'
2 'That flag is going to be first.'
3 'North Pole, here we come.'
4 '*Fram* is going to the Arctic.'
5 'Why are we bringing dogs with us?'
6 'Boys, I know you are unhappy.'
7 'It's a ski race, isn't it? And the English can't ski.'
8 'Are you going to win?'
9 'I know about dogs – they don't work in the Antarctic.'
10 'We need a lot of food – more than this.'

Chapters 4, 5 and 6 *Are these sentences true or false?*

1 The Norwegians put a wooden house on the ice.
2 Amundsen put a lot of flags beside his depots.
3 The ponies and dogs worked well together.
4 Scott wanted to kill the ponies.
5 All the Norwegians worked hard on their equipment.
6 Amundsen wanted to start south before Scott, because of the motor sledges.
7 Scott's men worked hard on their equipment.
8 The Norwegian cook, Lindstrøm, went south with the sledges.
9 Johansen was angry with Amundsen.

Chapters 7 and 8 *Who in the story:*

1 wrote an unhappy letter to his mother?
2 knew how to drive Scott's dogs?
3 nearly fell down a fifty metre hole?
4 drove the motor sledges?
5 skied up the mountains?
6 killed thirty dogs?
7 killed the ponies?
8 told Teddy Evans to leave his skis behind?
9 was the fifth man with Scott's sledge?

Chapters 9 and 10 *Who said or wrote this?*

1 'Good morning, Lindstrøm. Is our coffee ready?'
2 'This is a very bad day.'
3 'My poor, poor husband.'

4 'Am I going to lose these feet, Captain?'
5 'I'm going outside for a minute. I may be some time.'
6 'Please, remember us, and look after our families.'

B Working with language

Put together these beginnings and ends of sentences. Check your sentences in chapters 1, 2 and 3.

1 When Bjaaland and Amundsen went to the island,
2 It was difficult to get the dogs on the ship,
3 Let's go to the South Pole
4 When Scott came off the ship,
5 I don't like dogs,
6 When Oates first saw the ponies,
7 We ate our food in the room under the ponies,

a because they don't work in the Antarctic.
b so our table was often wet and dirty.
c because they were fat and strong.
d he was very unhappy.
e they saw dogs everywhere.
f a newspaper man walked up to him.
g before the British.

Use these words to join the two sentences together.
so and then because when but

1 Scott didn't make enough depots. His men were hungry.
2 The men's feet hurt. Their boots were bad.
3 The ponies started at ten o'clock. The dogs started at eleven.
4 The dogs started later. They ran faster.
5 Seven ponies died. They fell through the ice into the sea.

C Activities

1 Most of the men on the two expeditions wrote diaries. Choose one of the men, and write the diary of the journey, as he sees it.
2 Imagine you are a newspaper reporter who meets Amundsen and Bjaaland when they come back to Norway. *Either* a) act out this meeting, *or* b) write the report of your interview.
3 Oates wrote to his mother, and Scott wrote to his wife, before they died. Write one of these letters.

Glossary

alone if you are alone you are the only person there
ate past tense of 'to eat'
boot a big strong shoe
broken when an engine cannot move it is broken
buy to give money for something
came past tense of 'to come'
camp a place to stay
captain the most important man on a ship
could past tense of 'can'
dangerous not safe; it may kill or hurt you
depot a place to leave food and equipment
diary a book; you write your story in it
Earth the world; our planet; we all live on it
empty nothing in it; not full
equipment the things you need: skis, boots, sledges
flag every country has one – see picture on page 32
fog water in the air – you can't see through it
found past tense of 'to find'
gave past tense of 'to give'
go on not to stop
God (oh my God) something you say when you are very unhappy or afraid
hard difficult
hole where you can see through something
ice cold hard water; you can stand on it
island land with sea all round it
journey when you go a long way, you go on a journey
king the most important man in a country
knew past tense of 'to know'
last (at last) in the end
lay past tense of 'to lie'
left past tense of 'to leave'
lie (v) to go down on the ground
line one thing after another – the flags by the depot were in a line
look after (with animals) to give them food and see if they are OK
lost when you are lost you do not know where to go
map a drawing of the land – see picture on page 40
mistake when you do the wrong thing

motor sledge a sledge with an engine, like a car. It doesn't need men or dogs or ponies to pull it.
mountain a very big hill
plateau a high, flat place on a hill
Pole the South Pole the exact bottom of the Earth
pony a small horse
poor when you feel sorry for someone, you say 'poor man'
pull to make something move
race when two or more people try to be first
ran past tense of 'to run'
reach to arrive; to get somewhere
sat past tense of 'to sit'
saw past tense of 'to see'
ski (n) a long piece of wood to put your feet on to travel on the snow – see picture on page 20
ski (v) to use skis
skier a person who travels on skis
sledge something to carry food and equipment across the snow – see picture on page 30
snow cold white rain
snowstorm a lot of wind and a lot of snow
spoke past tense of 'to speak'
start to begin; to take the first step
stood past tense of 'to stand'
stupid not clever
temperature how hot or cold it is
tent a small house made of cloth – see picture on page 32
thought past tense of 'to think'
took past tense of 'to take'
travel to go a long way
unhappy not happy
went past tense of 'to go'
win to be first in a race
wind air that moves
wooden made of wood, from trees
wrote past tense of 'to write'